THE COAL ERA
IN THE UNITED STATES
A Study of Our Viable Alternatives

THE COAL ERA
IN THE UNITED STATES
A Study of Our Viable Alternatives

by
C.B. REED

ANN ARBOR SCIENCE
PUBLISHERS INC / THE BUTTERWORTH GROUP

Cover photo courtesy of James Whitney of The Peabody Coal Company, St. Louis, MO.

Library of Congress Catalog Card Number 81-68030
ISBN 0-250-40484-2

Butterworth, Ltd., Borough Green, Sevenoaks,
Kent, TN15 8PH, England

Preface

These pages were originally intended to be a chapter in a 1981 revision of the author's 1975 book *Fuels, Minerals and Human Survival* (Ann Arbor Science Publishers, Inc.), but as the work progressed it seemed impossible to bring it to a halt without reaching far beyond the original intent.

We have finally been satisfied to call a halt after answering two vital questions:

1. What will it cost to produce synthetic fuels from United States coals?
2. If we are going to proceed gradually from the Petroleum Era to the Coal Era in this country, what will be our energy mix at the middle of the next century?

We believe that the answers set forth here are reliable and that the reader will be satisfied with the documentation herein presented.

C. B. Reed

Acknowledgments

During the many revisions of this material, the continuing editorial assistance of my wife, Evelyn Roberts Reed, has been invaluable.

The encouragement and constructive criticism of many friends was very helpful. I am particularly grateful to Samuel P. Ellison, Jr. and Bernard B. Kinsey, who read the manuscript in its early stages and made suggestions for important changes.

The publisher's editorial staff also contributed substantially to the quality of the finished work.

C. B. Reed, an Austin, Texas, geologist, received his technical education at the Engineering School of the University of Virginia and the Graduate School of Harvard University.

In 1929 he went to work for one of the earliest geophysical consulting firms in the United States: Mason, Slichter and Gauld. Exploration programs were carried out for U.S. Steel, the M. A. Hanna Co., American Smelting & Refining Co. and United Verde Copper Co.

Mr. Reed was later employed as a Junior Geologist by the U.S. Geological Survey and went from there to become one of the pioneers in seismology for Shell Oil Company.

In 1941 he formed his own exploration company, which made it possible for him to retire in 1947.

In 1950 Mr. Reed returned to work as a consultant, covering the territory from New Orleans to Calgary for Newmont Oil Co., Southern Natural Gas Co., Cyprus Mines, Phelps Dodge Corp., North Central Oil Co., Argo Oil Co., Tenneco and others.

Before his retirement in 1967, he was a member of the Society of Exploration Geophysicists, American Association of Petroleum Geologists, American Institute of Mining Engineers, the American Association for the Advancement of Science and the Geological Society of America. He is a registered Professional Engineer in the state of Texas.

In March 1971 he published *Education and Catastrophe* (The San Felipe Press). Late in 1971 he acted as consultant to the NAS/NRC Committee on Radioactive Waste Management. In 1975 he published his second book, *Fuels, Minerals and Human Survival,* (Ann Arbor Science Publishers Inc.).

The viewpoints of the author do not necessarily coincide with those of the publisher. However, due to the interest in this controversial subject, we believe it reasonable to provide a platform for Mr. Reed's presentation.

Contents

1
Viable Choices

The world-wide consensus of economic geologists is that our affluent *Petroleum Era* will come to an end around the middle of the next century (Figure 6). To me this is a demonstrable fact, though it is derided as a hoax by many people, including some of our solid American citizens.

If it is indeed a fact, then we of the industrial nations of the world are faced with some hard choices, choices of two dimensions:

1. What can we depend on as long-term energy sources, sources for millennia to come?
2. In the meantime, what can we fall back on as interim sources of power?

In category (1) we do not have a wide variety to choose from, and the choices we do have are beset by a multitude of technical, political and economic problems.

(a) The Liquid Metal Fast Breeder Reactor (LMFBR) would extend the world's uranium resources from a century or less to several thousand years, but the industrial nations of the world cannot even agree that it should be built. Three prototypes are now operational [1] and a commercial plant is scheduled for 1983 completion [2], but the very concept is frightening to a

1

great many people, including some nuclear physicists [3] and some scientists of other disciplines [4, pp. 29-31].

(b) Power plants delivering electrical energy from nuclear fusion have received increasing attention since the U.S. exploded the first hydrogen bomb in 1952, but we are still a long way from success. Such plants would add a great deal to our long-term capabilities, but many physicists doubt that any net power output will ever be achieved by nuclear fusion.

(c) Many aspects of solar power progress slowly toward what may become the dominant source in another century [5]. It is the ultimate long-term source, limited only by the availability of the necessary hardware.

ASSISTANCE FROM THE SUN

Solar power also offers some modest help in category (2) for the short-term future [5,6].

Residential heating and cooling from direct sunlight can be in general public use within a decade if such a program is adequately funded. There are no difficult problems involved and the materials used are commonplace and abundant.

Roof-top solar systems to heat household water are now being manufactured in several U.S. states and in Israel, the U.S.S.R. and Japan.

In some parts of the U.S. and in Mexico, Africa, Colombia and India homemade and commercially manufactured solar cookers are in use.

Any municipality, or any profit-oriented corporation with a municipal and/or rural contract, should be able to get sufficient help to build a pyrolysis plant producing oil and/or gas and char from the hundreds of millions of tons of organic wastes we now "dispose of": manure; garbage; sewage solids; lawn and garden trash; paper; industrial wastes; wastes from lumbering, forestry and wood manufacturing; agricultural cellulose; plastics; old tires and miscellaneous urban refuse. One oil company and a half-dozen manufacturers of industrial equipment have completed their pilot-plant studies and are ready for demonstrations of commercial installations. This solar resource (biomass) is renewable and will certainly have a permanent place in future plans [7].

Electric power plants using the heat from direct sunlight can be built today, but I have no knowledge of any that are planned for the immediate future.

From offshore New England down the coast, across the Gulf and up the Texas Panhandle to the Aleutian Islands, 10 different areas could be developed for windpower (solar) electric systems; but this will be a slow development keyed by desperation as our Petroleum Era declines.

Thermal differences in sea water between the constantly warmed surface and the constantly cooled depths can also be made to yield (solar) electric power. Research and development continue, but I can't foresee any appreciable power production during this decade [5, pp. 123-139].

During the past decade, dozens of researchers all over the world have been hard at work trying to develop specific solar-cell approaches, all aimed at producing an "inexpensive, reliable, mass-producible solar photovoltaic cell" [5]. Such a cell certainly has a place in our future. Westinghouse Electric expects to provide demonstration photovoltaic modules in 1981 for California's two largest electrical utilities [8, p. 40d].

Photoelectric cells can be used on buildings, at ground central stations and in space; but just when they will be used we cannot say, for thousands of cells would be required and none of these systems are yet cost-effective.

Electrochemical photovoltaic cells may also be a part of our future [5] but they are farther removed from fruition.

Hydroelectric power is another indirect source of solar energy, but there is very little hydroelectric potential left within the United States. I cannot see that our ultimate production from this source will ever exceed 6% of our energy consumption in the U.S. (Figure 7).

INESCAPABLE DECISIONS

Geothermal sources also can be of some help in meeting the energy requirements of industrial nations under category (2). But in the post-petroleum era the large-scale immediate alternatives will be:

(a) Coal and its derivatives for those who have it or can pay for it, and/or:

(b) The nuclear industry's Light Water Reactors (LWR's) for those who have the fuel, the hardware and the knowledge to put these together. For those who have nothing but the money to pay, all of these can now be purchased as a package on the open market. The U.S. is fearful and lags behind, but Western Europe is pushing sales vigorously. A 1977 Franco-West German agreement [1] even foresees the export and licensing of LMFBR's with all of the hardware and the expertise needed to keep such plants operational.

2

Decisions Made

Of those countries who have made their choices, these facts are known:

South Africa has chosen to go for coal, synthetic fuels made from coal, and synthetic fuels made from renewable biomass [9]. Their ventures appear to be sound.

According to Sweden's eminent physicist Sten von Friesen, "Our energy mix will be 60% nuclear within the foreseeable future" [10]. They actually have a limited choice. They have neither coal nor oil nor gas, but they do have a considerable energy potential from renewable biomass.

Great Britain is fortunate. They have coal, oil and gas; and after 25 years of research and development they can build nuclear reactors whenever they choose to do so, including the LMFBR. A prototype fast breeder on the North coast of Scotland is fully operational.

France has jumped the gun on all of us, for after 25 years of reactor experience they are building the world's first LMFBR, a 1,200 Mw(e) plant scheduled to go on stream [2] in August 1983. If their homework has been properly done and the fast breeder is safe and efficient, then France will have achieved the first step toward a long-term energy future. They believe, while others doubt; but only time will prove what they have bought —affluence or catastrophe.

Russia is an enormous country with an enormous resource base. Like the U.S., it is still using a variety of energy sources, including LWR's similar to our own, and does not expect to build commercial LMFBR's during this century [11].

West Germany is very short on oil, and like many other Western nations it is making strenuous efforts to change its energy base to coal and nuclear power. In the strip-mining of its lignite, the largest reserves in Europe [12], it is showing the world just what can be done with a minimum of environmental degradation.

Brazil, with no important oil deposits, is going all out for an Alcohol Era as the Petroleum Era begins to fade. With a wealth of renewable biomass, the economic planners can add to this an abundance of coal and synfuels made from it, a hydroelectric network that presently supplies 90 to 95% of its electric power [13,14] and the possibility of oil production from extensive oil-shale deposits. There has been a lot of discussion of "going nuclear" with the help of West European expertise, but no final agreement has been reached with any supplier [1,13,14].

Japan has few natural resources, but an enormous ingenuity. They will flow with the tide. At the moment, they are importing Persian Gulf oil, West Virginia coal and Western European nuclear know-how. As worldwide oil production diminishes, they expect to make out with a coal-and-nuclear mix, changing gradually from LWR's [1] to commercial-scale LMFBR's through the 1990s.

3

Our Decision

The preceding covers the wide variety of choices available to those who have choices. If you now ask: "What of the United States?", I must express my belief that the Coal Era will replace the Petroleum Era in this country.

President Carter expressed this belief and a Democratic Congress backed him up. His only concession to a future need for nuclear reactors was expressed in his fiscal 1980 budget message calling for "substantial funding for research on the basic technologies, fuels, components and safety of the LMFBR".

President Reagan has decided that such funds should be provided, for our Clinch River breeder reactor [15], but beyond this point there are substantial in-house differences.

Our Secretary of Energy James B. Edwards believes that we should opt now for the Nuclear Era. Chairman S. David Freeman of the TVA supports him [16] and so does the Nuclear Regulatory Commission, which now proposes [17] to take away the only tools that citizens have in a democratic proceeding: the right of the public to require the NRC staff to produce detailed information about a power plant before a formal hearing opens.

Table I.   Identified Resources of U.S. Coal in Billions of Short Tons

Geographical Location	Lignite	Subbituminous	Bituminous	Anthracite	Total
Western	470	330	140	x	940
Midwestern	x	x	315	x	315
East & Southeast	x	x	290	25	315
Alaska	x	110	20	x	130
Totals	470	440	765	25	1,700[a]

	Recoverable Resources in Billions of Short Tons							
	Lignite		Subbituminous		Bituminous		Anthracite	Total
	Strip[a]	Shaft	Strip[a]	Shaft	Strip[a]	Shaft	Shaft	
Western[b]	35	175[c]	35	130	15	55	x	445[b]
Midwestern		x		x	15	150	x	165
East & Southeast		x		x	10	140	15	165
Alaska[d]		x	5	50	x	10	x	65
Totals	210		220		395		15	840[e]
Average Btu per ton	14 million		20 million		28 million		28 million	22.4 million
Q (Btu × 10^15)	2,940		4,400		11,060		420	18,800

[a] Paul Averitt's estimate [19] that 7½% of the Identified Resources can be strip-mined has been revised to 8%. At 85% recovery, about 14% of our *recoverable* coal will be strip-mined.

[b] More than 50% of our recoverable coal is in the arid Western states. Of this, almost 85% is either lignite or subbituminous coal with an average moisture content of 30%. This translates into 1.7 bbl of water per ton of coal. In plans for synthetic fuels production, this item may play a part.

[c] The deeper lignite is not cost-competitive at present. Some of it will ultimately be converted to SNG *in situ* at a thermal efficiency of about 40%.

[d] We assume that Alaskan coal will be used as a primary fuel and none will be converted to synthetic fuels.

[e] This is about 53% of Paul Averitt's 1973 estimate of Identified U.S. Resources [19].

Table II. Production [20] and Costs [21] of U.S. Coals

Year	Millions of Short Tons	Thousands of Btu per lb	$Q = $ Btu per Year $\times 10^{15}$	Wyoming Strip	Illinois Shaft	Pennsylvania Shaft
1957	520	13.0	13.5	90% subbituminous		bituminous
1958	430	13.0	11.3	@ 20.8 million		@ 28 million
1959	435	12.8	11.2	Btu per ton		Btu per ton
1960	435	12.8	11.1			
1961	420	12.8	10.8			
1962	440	12.8	11.3			
1963	475	12.8	12.2			
1964	505	12.7	12.9			
1965	525	12.7	13.4		Cost per unit, f.o.b. mines	
1966	545	12.6	13.9			
1967	565	12.6	14.2			
1968	565	12.5	14.0	@ $0.67	@ $1.30	@ $1.23
1969	570	12.4	14.3	per	per	per
1970	615	12.3	15.1	million	million	million
1971	560	12.1	13.7	Btu	Btu	Btu
1972	600	12.0	14.5			
1973	600	12.0	14.4			Shaft
1974	610	11.9	14.5	Strip		
1975	655	11.6	15.2	$14 per ton		$27 per ton
1976	685	11.6	15.9	Composite average—$21		
1977	705	11.5	16.2			
1978	695	11.5	16.0			
1979	770	11.4	17.5	$14 per ton	$36 per ton	$34 per ton
1980	825	11.4	18.8	$16 per ton	$18 per ton	$38 per ton
2010	Est. 2,000	11.2	44.8			

The House, meanwhile, strongly supports a synfuels program, and the Senate will back those ventures in which the operator will "put some money up front". But the Administration feels free to chop away at anything, including investments in synfuels, energy efficiency and renewable energy sources [18].

THE WRITER'S OPINION

I believe that our decision has been made and I am acting on that belief: *the Coal Era will replace the Petroleum Era in this country.* The energy corporations, the mining companies, the gas companies, the public utilities and the public itself have made this joint decision in the midst of a developing *de facto* moratorium on nuclear reactors.

The following pages were written to inform the public, and to furnish the active participants with data to answer their fundamental questions: how much coal; of what quality; where; at what cost? In Table I will be found: how much; what quality; and where. In Table II will be found production statistics and widespread cost estimates.

4

Synfuel Coal Costs

Basically, I have accepted Paul Averitt's 1973 estimates of Identified U.S. Coal Resources [19], but in
some geologic provinces these estimates have been revised upward in the light of more recent data. The estimates of recoverable resources as of January 1, 1981 are
my own. If these data are valid, then these computations are pertinent:

LIGNITE

At 14 million Btu per ton, Western lignite (brown
coal) has a gross oil equivalent of 2.45 bbl per ton, if
the product is equal to crude oil of 5.7 million Btu per
bbl. At 55% recovery, net oil equivalent is 1.35 bbl per
ton. At a competitive strip-mined price of $14 per ton,
probable coal cost would be about $10 per bbl of oil.
(Btu is a short term for British thermal unit, a universal
standard for measuring heat content.)

By the same criteria, this lignite has a gross equivalent of 14 Mcf of synthetic natural gas (SNG) per ton,
if we accept 1 million Btu per Mcf as normal. (An Mcf
of gas is 1000 cu ft, the standard unit of commerce.)
At 60% recovery, net equivalent is 8.4 Mcf per ton.

At $14 per ton of coal, coal cost would be about $1.70 per Mcf of gas.

HIGHER RANKS OF COAL

Strip- or shaft-mined Western coal at a weighted average of 20.8 million Btu per ton for subbituminous and bituminous grades, has a gross crude-oil equivalent of 3.65 bbl per ton. At 55% recovery, net oil equivalent is 2.00 bbl per ton. If strip-mined at $16 per ton, coal cost would be about $8 per bbl of oil. If shaft-mined at a competitive price of $26 per ton, coal cost should be about $13 per bbl of oil.

For synthetic natural gas production, this coal has a gross equivalent of 20.8 Mcf of gas per ton. At 60% recovery, net equivalent is 12.5 Mcf. If strip-mined at $16 per ton, coal cost would be about $1.30 per Mcf. If shaft-mined at $26 per ton, coal cost should be about $2.00 per Mcf.

HARD COALS

At 28 million Btu per ton, strip-mined or shaft-mined bituminous coal from the East, the Midwest and the Southeast has a gross oil equivalent of 4.90 bbl per ton. At 55% recovery, net crude-oil equivalent is 2.70 bbl per ton. If strip-mined at $18 per ton, probable coal cost is about $7 per bbl of oil. If shaft-mined at $38 per ton, probable coal cost is about $14 per bbl of oil.

The same coal has a gross equivalent of 28 Mcf of SNG per ton. At 60% recovery, net equivalent is 16.8 Mcf per ton of coal. If strip-mined at $18 per ton, coal

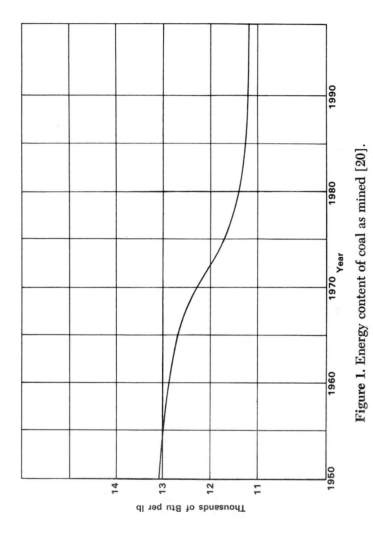

Figure 1. Energy content of coal as mined [20].

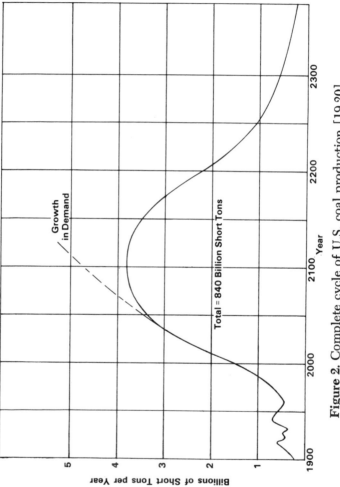

Figure 2. Complete cycle of U.S. coal production [19,20].

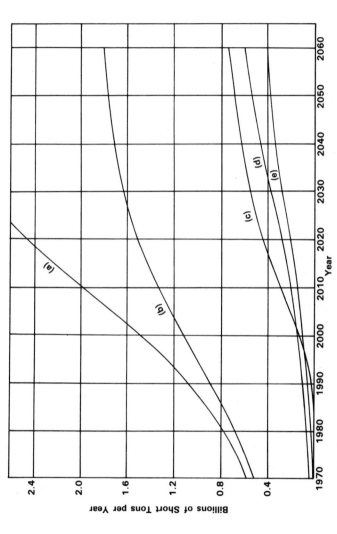

Figure 3. Production and projected use of U.S. coals. (a) Mined (see Figure 2); (b) burned; (c) to syncrude; (d) exported; (e) to SNG.

cost would be in the neighborhood of $1.10 per Mcf. If shaft-mined at $38 per ton, probable coal cost would be about $2.30 per Mcf.

WEIGHTED AVERAGES

In the U.S., economics, politics, tax write-offs, ecological judgments, metallurgical coal requirements and statutory restrictions will govern just what coals will become synthetic fuels in the immediate future and in the decades yet to come. Meanwhile, in the absence of definitive decisions, I believe we are quite justified in making computations from weighted averages based on grades of available coal and their geological and geographic occurrences.

On the evidence at hand in 1980, we estimated that the recoverable coal resources of the U.S. are approximately 840 billion tons. However, if we accept (a) that the deeper lignites and (d) the Alaskan coals (Table I) are not presently available for conversion to synthetic fuels, we are left with a synfuel-plant potential of some 600 billion tons of coal. The previously tabulated tonnages and the above recoveries and costs indicate that:

If 6% of the available coal is Western strip-mined lignite at $14 per ton, this coal-cost would be $10 per bbl of oil or $1.70 per Mcf of gas.

If 8% of the available coal is Western strip-mined bituminous or subbituminous coal at $16 per ton, this coal-cost would be $8 per bbl of oil or $1.30 per Mcf of gas.

If 4% of the available coal is strip-mined in the Midwest, the East and the Southeast at $18 per ton, this coal-cost would be about $7 per bbl of oil or $1.10 per Mcf of gas.

If just over 30% of the available coal is shaft-mined in the Western states at a competitive price of $26 per ton, this coal-cost would be about $13 per bbl or $2.00 per Mcf.

If just over 50% of the available coal is shaft-mined in the East, the Midwest and the Southeast at $38 per ton, this coal-cost would be $14 per bbl of oil or $2.30 per Mcf of gas.

EFFICIENCIES AND COSTS

Overall efficiencies of hypothetical plants are impossible to judge. For this reason I have used rock-bottom estimates, though there are reliable ones which indicate that recoveries from U.S. plants may eventually be considerably higher:

The American Gas Association states that in a pilot plant using Illinois coal (28 million Btu per ton) a thermal efficiency of 68% was obtained in the recovery of gas by treating coal with hydrogen under pressure at a high temperature.

The *Scientific Encyclopedia* [22] estimates that the Lurgi process, treating coal with oxygen and steam, is 68 to 70% efficient in the recovery of synthetic natural gas (SNG).

The same encyclopedia states that South Africa's syncrude plant is converting a poor grade of coal into an acceptable grade of crude oil at an efficiency of approximately 62%.

Since we cannot estimate specific recoveries or specific unit costs for synfuel plants not yet designed, to be built in areas not yet known, weighted averages of costs and recoveries are certainly justified. These data, embracing every known grade of coal from all U.S. coal provinces, indicate that:

We can expect to recover somewhat more or somewhat less than 2.35 bbl of oil or 15 Mcf of gas per ton of coal.

Coal-costs will be somewhat more or somewhat less than $13 per bbl of oil or $2.00 per Mcf of gas.

5

Our Limitations

Eight hundred and forty billion tons is a lot of coal; it is, in fact, a "vast reserve of energy" as so often stated in the public press. But the well-documented fact is that there is no conceivable way that we can get U.S. coal out of the ground fast enough to catch up with our inevitable shortfall of petroleum liquids and natural gas. We will need assistance from the entire energy spectrum (Figures 4, 5 & 7).

To my great surprise, I find that in the technical publications we have come to rely upon, there is no universally accepted energy equivalent for a bbl of crude oil. The API [23] uses the figure of 5.8 million Btu per bbl; Perry and Chilton [24] find by laboratory analysis that specific crude oils may vary from 5.6 to 5.9 million Btu per bbl; Exxon [25] states that the heat equivalent of a bbl of oil is 5.55 million Btu. From these equally reliable sources, we conclude that a bbl of crude oil is equivalent to approximately 5.7 million Btu.

Petroleum liquids are something else again. As presently consumed in the U.S., they are a mixture of domestic and imported crude oils, lease-condensate from gas wells, natural-gas liquids extracted at processing plants, and imported refined petroleum products. Based on a weighted average of energy content ranging from

19

5.6 to 6.3 million Btu per bbl, petroleum liquids over a year's time will approximate 5.75 million Btu per bbl. On this basis, our 18,800 Q of coal is equivalent to 3,270 billion bbl of petroleum liquids. (One Q is a quadrillion Btu.)

COAL IN PERSPECTIVE

That's a lot of liquids; but by the very nature of the resource, most of it is in trust for future generations, for the coal industry is not geared for crash expansion programs.

In 1918 about 900 thousand underground coal miners working 60 hours a week produced about 2 tons per day per man.

To make coal competitive with oil and gas, billions of dollars were subsequently spent in coal-mine mechanization. In 1976, 202 thousand miners on a 40-hour week produced an average of 9 tons per day per man underground and 26 tons in strip mines [20]. Coal became cost-competitive; yet the abundance of clean-burning oil and gas made it difficult to increase the production of coal. Our 1975 production barely equaled our 1942 production, which was just slightly higher than our production in 1918 (Figure 2). Now, in 1981, our need for coal to replace other fossil fuels is acute, but the coal industry is "buried under tons of problems" [26]. Endemic labor troubles have created an uncertainty of supply which translates into an uncertain demand.

One typical industry response has been to look to foreign sources. Exxon has agreed to split with the Colombian government the estimated $3 billion cost of a new mine, railroad and port facilities [8, p. 40] to exploit a "vast coal property" in the remote Guajira area of northeast Colombia.

Meanwhile in West Virginia [27] "both talk and coal are plentiful", while the miners demonstrate that this is the one U.S. industry in which unemployment and strikes can coexist.

Approximately 1000 big mines produced 85% of our 1980 coal production of 825 million tons [20] of which about 90 million tons [26] were exported, up 50 million [28] from 1978. Five thousand "bank mines" in 26 states produced the other 15% [20]. It is quite possible that within the next 30 years, at enormous capital expense, the expansion of our present mines and the opening of hundreds of large new ones could increase the total U.S. production in 2010 to 2.00 billion tons per year, an increase of 1.18 billion tons over 1980 (Figure 2). Some other estimates are higher, but I cannot accept them.

If export rates continue upward as expected [29] then 200 million tons is a reasonable expectation for 2010 exports, leaving us with 1,800 million tons for domestic use. If we burn 1,350 million tons as primary fuel at 22.4 million Btu per ton (Figure 1), then 30.2 Q (Btu $\times$ 10^{15}) will be added to our 2010 energy consumption to bolster up the sagging production of petroleum liquids and natural gas (Figure 7).

If we are able to build 30 to 35 synthetic crude-oil (syncrude) plants to process a total of 300 million tons of coal per year, we can produce the equivalent of about 700 million bbl of petroleum liquids per year in 2010 (Figure 4). This is more than 50% of our anticipated domestic production during that year.

If half that number of plants are built to process 150 million tons of coal into synthetic natural gas (SNG)

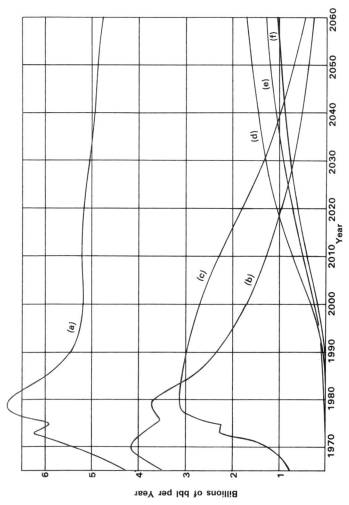

Figure 4. U.S. production, imports and consumption of petroleum liquids. (a) Used; (b) produced; (c) imported. Synthetics from (d) coal; (e) biomass; (f) shales and sands.

during 2010, we can expect to produce about 2.25 trillion cubic feet during that year (Figure 5). This is more than 25% of our projected production for 2010. By that time it is almost certain that a substantial amount of SNG will be produced by *in situ* treatment of coal beds which are never mined. By the proper techniques we can also produce usable liquids from this unmined–coal gas [30], and this we will certainly do.

COAL HAZARDS

To the extent that our expanding technology permits, all possible effort should be made to improve and expand the use of *in situ* recovery of synfuels and minimize the mining and processing of coal; for though we know that 25,000-tons-a-day mines and processing plants are possible, they are monstrous assemblages requiring enormous effort and enormous capital investment. In comparison, our 300 largest coal mines averaged only 4,200 tons per day each in the decade of the seventies [31]. We are also faced with these very real problems when considering a three-fold expansion of U.S. coal mining: both the mining and the consumption of coal are ecologically and personally hazardous.

The hazards of mining include acid mine-drainage; erosion of strip-mined hillsides; silting of streams; leaching of pollutants from accumulated wastes; mine fires and explosions; subsidence over mined-out areas; and the occupational diseases and deaths of the miners.

It is generally accepted that the burning of all coals will cause some ecological and personal damage. Even synfuel plant processes using coal will be damaging to some extent, for in all synfuel methods some volatile

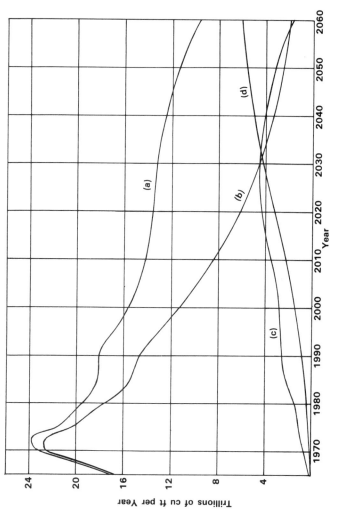

Figure 5. U.S. Production, imports and consumption of natural gas. (a) Consumption; (b) natural production; (c) imports [25]; (d) synthetic natural gas.

and some particulate matter will be vented to the atmosphere.

Chemical pollution embraces, but is not restricted to, carbon dioxide, sulfur dioxide and nitrogen oxides. In many areas the burning of coal has led to an irritating acid rainfall engendered by sulfur dioxide in the air. Furthermore, the heat generated by all power plants leads to widespread thermal pollution, which may in time be more than we can tolerate. The greenhouse effect of increasing carbon dioxide in the atmosphere could significantly raise global temperatures within a few decades [32,33].

Particulate pollution covers a wide variety of substances. From all coal-fired plants more than 40 trace elements are partially vented to the air and partially buried in sludge pits. Many of these elements are needed by industry in small quantities and have their greatest reserves in the coal we are so anxious to burn. Equally true, but less well known, is the fact that the burning of coal, including lignite, releases to the air significant traces of the radioactive solids uranium, thorium and radium, and the radioactive gas radon [34]. The ashes of some lignites, in fact, could be commercial ores of uranium (0.40%) and contain significant quantities of molybdenum, vanadium, arsenic, germanium, selenium, cobalt, beryllium, bismuth, lead, mercury and zirconium [35].

SULFUR CONTENT

Ironically, many recently constructed electric power plants which were equipped with scrubbers in order to burn high-sulfur coal, have not only reduced sulfur dioxide emissions to close to zero [36, p. 47], but are also polluting the air with fewer radioactive pollutants than those plants which elected to skip the scrubbers and contract for low-sulfur Western coal [34]. In making these pro-Western decisions, someone's calculations must have been off-scale. Pollution control systems for 4%-sulfur coal may add 25% to power plant costs [36], but freight costs for low-sulfur coal from Western mines will soon make scrubber investments very attractive. The city of Austin, Texas and its partners elected to go the Western-coal route for their latest generators and their 1981 freight bill will be about $75 million [37]. During 40 years of rising freight rates, that will total quite a sum.

Ironically, the motive power for these coal trains will be scarce diesel fuel, a fuel probably made in a Texas refinery from Texas crude oil. This situation, brought on by the low cost of diesel fuel during the fifties and sixties, has now brought about a widespread discussion of the advisability of electrifying our railroads with electric power from coal-fired generating plants.

It may well happen. Do not, in fact, be surprised in this Wizard-of-Oz era to find some day that lignite-fired Texas plants are furnishing the electricity to haul Wyoming coal on its last lap through the state of Texas to be burned in Texas power plants!

6

The Twenty-First Century

Many economic geologists, including the writer [4], have serious doubts about the long-term availability of the many irreplaceable metals and minerals necessary for industrial hardware. However, if we are determined to continue with the expansion of our use of coal, whatever the human or ecological costs, the future will take this shape:

Eighty years from now, in 2060, the world's supply of natural petroleum liquids will be virtually exhausted (Figure 6). At that time, if our capital, our expertise and the metals and minerals available are equal to the task, the coal production in the United States should be 3.54 billion tons per year (Figure 2) and exports about 600 million tons [39].

If 1,800 million tons are burned as primary fuel at 22.4 million Btu per ton, this would add 40.3 Q to our aggregate energy supply (Figure 7) and would be the largest single source of U.S. energy in 2060.

If we can build 50 more standard syncrude plants (at 25 thousand tons of coal per day each) and process a total of 740 million tons per year in all these plants (Figure 3), we should be able to add 1.72 billion bbl of petroleum liquids per year to our available supply (Figure 4). At this time, these and other synthetic fuels

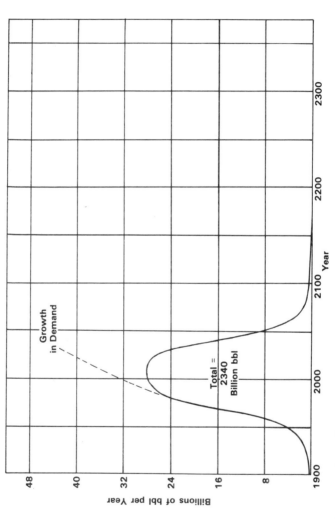

Figure 6. Complete cycle of world production of petroleum liquids, after Ryman et al. [38].

should be supplying 85% of our available petroleum liquids. *The Petroleum Era will be over.* We who were born early in this century saw the beginning of it. Many of those born in 1981 will live to see the end of it.

If we can build the plants to process the remaining 400 million tons per year into SNG, we can add 6.0 trillion cu ft per year to our natural gas supply (Figure 5). This is more than 60% of our estimated available supply for 2060. If some of this gas can be produced *in situ*, then we may decide (a) to mine less coal or (b) to use part of the 400 million tons in the petrochemical industry.

Our "vast reserves" of coal are no myth and they can take up a large part of the slack as petroleum production declines (Figure 7), but we will pay a price for their use. Just how high this price will be depends upon our technical ingenuity and the measure of our regard for human well-being and ecological degradation.

SYNFUELS IN PERSPECTIVE

Synfuels are not new. The first plant making gas from coal was built in Europe in 1802, and in the early part of this century every large American city had its own coal-gas plant. In this country in the 1950s there were hundreds of small packaged gasifying systems supplying "producer gas" to industrial plants requiring gas-fired furnaces.

These early systems were mothballed when cheap natural gas became plentiful, but now the situation has been reversed [40, p. 79]. With natural gas priced above $7 per Mcf in many U.S. areas, engineering contractors are once again finding that there is a growing demand

for small packaged systems to meet individual plant requirements, for the input nozzle at the combustion zone
can't tell much difference between producer gas and
natural gas, since they both burn optimum mixtures of
gas-plus-air. Producer gas, at 150 Btu per cu ft, measures
about 75 Btu per cu ft as fired with air in a 1:1 ratio.
Natural gas, at 1000 Btu per cu ft, measures 90 to 100
Btu as fired with air in a 10:1 ratio of air to gas [40,
p. 82].

There are still no large-scale commercial SNG plants
in the U.S. There are only a few in Europe and one in
South Africa using the Lurgi process (developed in the
1930s) in conjunction with "the new coal technology".

Neither do we have large-scale commercial syncrude
plants, though more than two dozen small-scale synfuel projects are now operating or being constructed
around the country [41]. Insofar as I know, the only
commercial syncrude plant operating today is in South
Africa [22].

From a poor grade of coal averaging 8,300 Btu per lb,
the operators are said to be recovering 1.78 bbl of oil
per ton of coal, an efficiency of about 60% if the oil
is of standard crude-oil grade, 5.7 million Btu per bbl.

Their secret process, involving retorting with both
oxygen and steam (the SASOL process) is presently
limited to one plant making 24,000 bbl per day [9] at
a stated cost of $17 per bbl. No breakdown of this cost
is available, but the logical assumption is that it covers
both the raw material costs and the operating costs of
the plant. Whether an allowance is made for amortiza-
tion of plant costs is not known, but their plans for two
more plants make it possible to estimate the per-bbl cost
of this capital item:

The two new plants are expected to produce a total

of 88,000 bbl of oil per day from 50,000 tons of coal. With plant costs of $5.8 billion amortized over 40 years, the capital costs per bbl would be about $4.50, assuming that government money is used and no interest charges are assessed. Even if the capital cost should be added, a total of $21.50 per bbl is still well below the current OPEC price of $35.

Just to show that South Africa intends to lead the way into the era beyond the Petroleum Era, they also plan to make wood alcohol (methanol) from wood and casava; ethyl alcohol (ethanol) from sugar cane and an acceptable diesel fuel from sunflower seeds.

DOWNHILL IN THE U.S.

These are South Africa's answers to necessity, for they have no indigenous petroleum and are forced to pay the highest spot-market prices for the oil they import. From all three SASOL plants they expect to get about half of their oil requirements in 1982 [42].

In the U.S. a dozen or more coal-conversion processes are in various stages of research and development and at least a dozen energy corporations plan to use them —*when they have to.* These have been plushy times for the major oil companies, with enormous profits being made from $30+ OPEC oil and $1.20 gasoline, but the handwriting on the wall is now plain for all to see (Figure 6): shortages of supply are not far around the corner [43] and only a determined synthetic-fuel program can make up the deficiency (Figure 4).

With a few exceptions, I agree with Exxon's 1979 estimates for the future [25]. My data point to the following conclusions:

Whether by OPEC decisions abroad or Administration decisions at home, or both, foreign oil will be less and less obtainable in the decades to come. For the year 2000, 52% of our declining consumption may be met by imports, but it's all downhill after that.

Continuing the present decline in production, only 33% of our year-2000 consumption can be met by domestic production, compared to 54% in 1980. If imports *can* supply 52% of our consumption, we may be able to fill the other 15% with synthetic fuels. Even so, our total oil supply, which almost doubled from 1960 to 1980, will decline by more than 17% during the next 20 years. After that, we could almost hold our own with a wide variety of syncrudes (Figure 4).

7

Questions and Answers

It would seem that the decade of "have to" is now on us. Our energy crisis has been growing for seven years, and still the favored boiler fuel is natural gas or fuel oil. During those years, the indecision of Congress and the Administration has forced our energy corporations into an acceptance of the status quo beneath a blanket of extreme uncertainty. Like many other things, an energy policy has been "just around the corner". Bills pending in Congress and imminent Agency regulations have been discussed to death while our "greedy energy corporations" waited—and profited.

The waiting is now over. On April 2, 1980, the "windfall profits" tax bill was signed into law. Originally conceived as an energy bill to encourage conservation, improve mass transit and develop alternative fuels, the tax was turned by Congress into the largest general-revenue Act ever passed. Specific funds are allocated for specific purposes; but these allocations are not binding, for all the new revenue will go into the Treasury's general fund and more legislation will be required before any of this money can be spent for any specific purpose [44, p. 73].

This "windfall" may be the only chance we will ever have to start paying off the national debt, get out from

under annual interest payments of $90 billion and oper-
ate the federal government within its income; but I
have not heard a whisper out of Washington. Congress
has instead raised the national debt ceiling close to a
trillion dollars.

I know that this tax money is now being paid into the
federal Treasury in large amounts; I know because I am
paying a part of it myself, month by month. I am a
royalty owner on a small scale, and in 1980 after the
Act was passed my "windfall profits" tax was 24% of
my gross royalty income. I would like to think that this
money will serve some useful purpose.

"How to spend the windfall-tax revenues could become an annual battle on Capitol Hill", observes a Wall-
Street analyst who monitors the oil industry [44, p. 73].
If this indeed becomes a political fact, then the tax
would be little more than a windfall bonanza for every
legislator's pet project. It could become, as some sus-
pect, "a cruel joke" [45] and an enormous upward push
on inflation.

THE APPARENT ANSWERS

Be that as it may, it does take our energy corporations
out of limbo and it does appear to answer the three
questions uppermost in their minds:

1. Will the initial proposal for an $88 billion govern-
ment corporation, the "Energy Security Corporation", put the federal government into the synfuels business? Negative. No such provision was
included in the Act.
2. Will the builders of synthetic-fuel plants have any

aid from the government? Positive. (a) The fiscal 1980 budget provided $248 million for research and development on processes for making syncrude and SNG from coal. (b) On November 19, 1979 the Senate approved a $20 billion 5-year package of incentives for synfuels development [44, p. 72]. On May 21, 1980, a Senate–House conference committee agreed on specific terms to provide $20 billion in backup funds, a collection of loan, purchase and price guarantees, that would induce private corporations to produce synthetic fuels from coal, shale and even wood chips and corn [46]. On June 26, 1980, the House passed the bill [47] and sent it to the President for his signature. He promptly signed it and the Act is now law, though President Reagan proposes in his fiscal 1982 budget to cut a few billion from the $20 billion in "backup funds". I await with interest the results of this "pump priming". (c) The "windfall profits" Act does not name a figure, but some tax credits will undoubtedly be allowed for synfuel plants. (d) The tentative allocations of "windfall profits" taxes indicate that 15%, an estimated $34 billion, will be spent for "energy development and mass transit", in ratios unspecified. Our energy corporations will get some of that.

3. Will the revenue Act leave them enough capital to build synthetic-fuel plants out of profits? Positive. The "windfall profits" tax is designed to soak up part of the extra revenue that oil companies will have as government price ceilings are lifted on domestic oil [44, p. 71]. Over the next 10 years the federal government expects to collect about $220 billion in windfall taxes, and another $350

billion in increased corporate income taxes plus higher gross royalties that will come in from federal oil lands.

This sounds like the kiss of death, but industry spokesmen estimate [44, p. 73] that even after paying the increased taxes and royalties, the oil industry will have additional after-tax revenues of $220 billion over the next 10 years as domestic oil prices rise to world levels. Even if this estimate is too high (and it may be) the answer to question (3) is still: "positive".

8

Corporate Plans

SNG FROM COAL

Meanwhile there is a lot of talk and some action on synthetic fuels. Late in 1972 [4, p. 108], El Paso Natural Gas Company filed an application with the Federal Power Commission (FPC) to build a $420 million plant to produce 250 million cu ft per day of synthetic natural gas (SNG) from New Mexico coal. In January of 1980 I called their El Paso office to find out what progress had been made. When it was clear what I wanted to know, I was connected with the "synthetic fuels division". No plant has been built, but I was authorized to say that: "We plan to build a plant to make SNG".

Several years ago the Commonwealth Edison Company of Chicago announced plans to gain experience with coal gasification by installing three Lurgi units [48].

The American Gas Association, Bituminous Coal Research, Inc., Consolidation Coal Company and the Institute of Gas Technology have each completed successful pilot-plant operations of their own synfuel processes and are ready to move on to demonstration and/or commercial plants [22,49].

Sales from the first proposed U.S. commercial SNG

plant have been approved by the Federal Energy Regulatory Commission [50]. American Natural Resources Company, a consortium of five companies, proposes to build a $1.4 to $1.6 billion plant in Mercer County, North Dakota to make 125 million cu ft per day, at 970 Btu per cu ft, from 14,000 tons of strip-mined lignite [51]. Start-up is estimated for 1984 using the Lurgi process, which is still the only demonstrably commercial method. Plant specifications include a steam plant, an oxygen plant and a methanation (catalytic converter) unit. Provision is also made to convert the unavoidable by-products into salable commodities.

The Lurgi Company, Germany's pioneer in the gasification of coal, has perfected its techniques to upgrade the gas to standard-grade SNG and to convert this gas to methanol if a liquid product is desired [52, p. 2].

Texaco is currently advertising on TV commercials that they expect to make "clean gas from dirty coals", presumably at a profit. Specifically they plan to start construction in 1981 on a $300 million plant in California [52, p. 8], in partnership with Southern California Edison. If their calculations are correct, this demonstration plant will yield gas for an electric power plant plus syncrude for Texaco's refineries.

Texaco and Transwestern Pipeline Company [53] have agreed to study the feasibility of a gasification plant in Wyoming.

Gulf Oil Corporation has announced that it plans to begin construction of a demonstration plant in 1981 to produce "gas and liquid products" from 6,000 tons per day of high-sulfur Eastern coal. At 50–60% recovery, such a plant will yield about 16,000 bbl per day of liquids or liquid equivalent [52, p. 2]. Completion is scheduled for early 1984.

In 1980 in Wyoming, Gulf, sponsored by the Department of Energy (DOE) to the extent of $13.5 million, demonstrated that test-burning of a steeply dipping coal seam with pure oxygen could produce a nitrogen-free gas which can be converted to usable petroleum liquids. The competitive economics are stated to be good [30] for *in situ* conversion.

LIQUIDS FROM COAL

To my certain knowledge, Exxon (Humble) has been working on synfuel processes for a number of years. Late in 1979 C. C. Garvin, Jr., Exxon's Chairman, stated [54] that the corporation is "at the point of seriously considering commercial ventures" in synthetic fuels. In a company public relations release [25, p. 12] they state that "645 million tons of coal are forecast to be used in the manufacture of synthetic fuels in the year 2000". They further state that "In Exxon planning studies, synthetic fuels volumes range from 4 to 6 million bbl a day oil equivalent in 2000".

"However," they go on to say, "to achieve this level of production will require a national resolve to aggressively develop synthetic fuels. Such a resolve does not yet clearly exist, and any projection of future synthetic production levels is subject to considerable variation" [25, p. 18].

I agree that "such a resolve does not yet clearly exist", but this much seems certain: Exxon and many other energy corporations will, in their own good time, produce synthetic fuels from coal and from other sources as well, for they have no viable alternative.

TVA Directors have authorized the initial plant design [53] for a 20,000-tons-a-day coal conversion plant to produce the equivalent of 50,000 bbl of oil per day when completed in 1989. Cost is estimated at $1 to $2 billion.

It has been reported [55] that Mobil Oil Corporation has developed the "Mobil M" process to convert natural gas into gasoline via methanol. A pilot plant is now being built in Germany.

According to Ashland Synthetic Fuels, Inc. (Ashland Oil Company) their $300 million experimental plant in Catlettsburg, Kentucky began producing syncrude from coal [56] in June of 1980 by a hydrogenation process developed by Hydrocarbon Research, Inc. Sponsors of the pilot project include the State of Kentucky, DOE, Conoco, Mobil, Stanolind and the Electric Power Research Institute.

Also in Kentucky, Texas Eastern Corporation plans a SASOL-type plant and W. R. Grace & Co. plans to build a giant facility using the "Mobil M" process [55].

In mid-1980 in another report entitled "The Role of Synthetic Fuels in the United States Energy Future", a report made available to the *Los Angeles Times* [57], Exxon proposes a $500 billion oil-shale industry to produce 8 million bbl of syncrude per day and a $300 billion coal-conversion industry to produce liquid and gaseous fuels equivalent to 7 million bbl per day. Raising the money, says Exxon, "is within the capabilities of private companies", and the goal can be achieved within 30 years. Admittedly this is a highly ambitious program, but Exxon states that it is not beyond achievement "by a determined America".

This is neither the time nor the place for an argument with Exxon; but I must say this: the estimates the reader will find within these pages are the maximum estimates that I consider realistically attainable.

SYNCRUDE FROM OIL SHALES

The Oil Shale Corporation (TOSCO) in a joint venture with Atlantic Richfield Company, Ashland Oil, Inc. and Shell Oil Company has completed pilot-plant studies at 25 tons of oil-shale per day and demonstration-plant studies at 1,000 tons per day and is ready now to move on to the construction and operation of 6 in-line commercial units processing a total of 66,000 tons of shale per day to produce almost 50,000 bbl of oil per day [58, pp. 47-64]. Their problems will be two-fold: where to find cooling-water; and where to put the spent shale.

In June of 1972, the Occidental Petroleum Corporation began experimental *in situ* retorting of oil shales near DeBeque, Colorado [58, pp. 73-81]. Seven underground retorts were fired with recoveries of 20 to 60% of the oil in place [59]. The corporation states [31] that the process is successful and they plan a 30,000-bbl-a-day plant here [58, p. 79] in partnership with Tenneco Oil Company.

This *in situ* process has some distinct advantages, but it also has some tricky problems [59]: the technology is less capital-intensive than mining-and-retorting and a 30,000-bbl-a-day plant will provide enough by-product gas to produce 200 Mw(e) of power for community use [58, p. 79]. Though underground retorting requires no water, seepage of ground water through the used retorts yields a quantity of highly polluted water. Part of this can be used in surface-retorting the 25% of the shale which is mined to create voids, and a part can be purified for steam-electric use; but a very troublesome residue is still left.

Also tested through the pilot-plant stage are *in situ*

processing methods developed by Phillips Petroleum, Cities Service Oil Company, Marathon Oil Company and Texaco [58, p. 12].

Near Rio Blanco, Colorado, Gulf and another oil company have already invested $250 million in lease bonuses and engineering studies preparatory to the construction of a $100 million demonstration plant for the surface retorting of oil shales [30].

Small-scale tests of Kentucky and Ohio oil-shales by Pyramid Minerals indicate that recoveries as high as 25 gallons of oil per ton of shale can be obtained in Allis-Chalmers rotary kilns [52, p. 1]. The Institute of Gas Technology also has a process in the research-and-development stage.

OTHER PLANS

Hearings for $1 billion conversion plants began in 1980 in Morgantown, West Virginia, in Owensboro, Kentucky and in the state of Texas [36, p. 49].

In May of 1980 Continental Oil Company announced in television commercials that they plan to spend upward of $230 million to expand their coal production.

Virginia's Coal & Energy Commission is recommending to the state legislature the creation of a state synfuels authority to work with industry in shaping proposals for DOE assistance on synfuels projects in Virginia [52, p. 8].

9

Plant Costs and Operating Costs

SYNCRUDE PLANTS

The only known plant costs for the commercial production of syncrude from coal are the costs of the new plants contracted for in the Union of South Africa. A contract has been let for 2 plants at $2.9 billion each to process 25,000 tons of coal per day per plant, each plant designed to produce 44,000 bbl of synthetic crude oil per day at the rate of 1.78 bbl per ton of coal [9].

In the U.S. a plant processing 25,000 tons of coal per day should produce 50,000 to 60,000 bbl of oil per day. We have no such plants and we have very few recent estimates of costs in the U.S. *Time* [60] estimates $1 to $3 billion for a coal-liquefaction plant to produce 50 to 100 thousand bbl a day. The *Oil & Gas Journal*, quoting Exxon [54], estimates a 50,000-bbl-a-day plant at $3 to $4 billion and a 100 thousand-bbl-a-day plant at $5 billion. The U.S. Congress [46] estimates the cost of a 50,000-bbl-a-day plant at $2.5 billion. Richard J.

Barnet [61] offers a conservative estimate of $3.5 billion for this decade.

Comparing these estimates with the contracts for South Africa's 25,000-tons-of-coal-per-day plants, it is reasonable to estimate that a plant in the U.S. to process 25,000 tons of American coal per day, and produce 50,000 to 60,000 bbl of oil per day, would cost approximately $3.5 billion.

If in the year 2010 we have 300 million tons of U.S. coal per year to run through such plants (Figure 3) we would need more than 30 of them at $3.5 billion each, a total capital investment of about $115 billion to produce 1.9 million bbl per day, or 700 million bbl per year (Figure 4).

There is much current talk of accelerated tax write-offs to encourage construction of new industrial plants. This may or may not happen, but even at the presently estimated 16-year write-off (IRS) two or three dozen major corporations in the 46% tax bracket (IRS) could do this out of otherwise-taxable profits.

Forty years' production for each proposed syncrude plant would be about 860 million bbl of oil. If plant costs of $3.5 billion are charged against this production, then about $4 per bbl would amortize the plant costs.

I have no real basis for estimating the operating costs of these plants, for none exist in the Western world of highly paid union labor. These plants would produce about 20 million bbl of oil per year each. I cannot visualize a payroll larger than 1000 men at $50 per day each, nor a maintenance cost of more than $20 million per year per plant. On this basis, operating and maintenance costs would approximate $2 per bbl of syncrude output.

SNG PLANTS

There is even less basis for estimating plant costs and operating costs for SNG plants. In 1972 we had a bona fide estimate of $420 million to produce 250 million cu ft per day; in 1973 an estimate of $350 million for the same output; and in 1974 an estimate of $300 million [62] and another of $500 million [63]. In 1979 a permit was requested to build a 125-million-cu-ft-per-day plant for $1.5 billion [50]. At a net recovery of 8.4 Mcf per ton from lignite, this $1.5 billion plant would use about 15,000 tons per day. On this basis, our standard plant processing 25,000 tons per day would cost $2.5 billion. The TVA's recent estimate [53] would translate into $1.875 billion for a 25,000-tons-a-day plant. Quadrupling the earliest estimates and adding an inflationary increase of 30% to the latest ones, the indicated price tag for a SNG plant processing 25,000 tons of coal a day is $2.5 billion.

At 60% recovery, the weighted average for all U.S. coals is about 15 Mcf per ton of coal (15,000 cu ft per ton). On this basis, each plant would produce 375 thousand Mcf per day, 137 million Mcf per year, and 5.475 billion Mcf during the 40-year life of the plant. If plant costs of $2.5 billion are charged against this production, then we must add about 45¢ per Mcf to our SNG costs for plant amortization. If we estimate plant operating-and-maintenance costs at $19 to $20 million a year, then we must add another 15¢ per Mcf.

10

Accessory Raw Materials

Synthetic-fuel plants processing coal will yield a variety of products; but whatever the plant or the product, varying amounts of water and/or oxygen and/or hydrogen will be required in the process. The cost of these materials will constitute 15 to 20% of the total cost of the final products, whatever they may be.

Some plants will produce low-Btu synthesis gas (CO + H_2) for boiler fuel, others will proceed from this to the production of high-Btu synthetic natural gas (CH_4) for domestic and industrial use; others will be built and operated primarily for the production of synthetic crude oil (syncrude). Still other plants will be hybrids, yielding gas and/or syncrude and/or coal-derived industrial chemicals. Whatever the choice, designers will need to know the unit costs of accessory raw materials as well as the unit coal-cost, plant costs, and operating-and-maintenance costs.

STEAM COSTS

To turn water at 100 degrees C into steam at the same temperature requires 539 calories per gram of water

[22]. This is equivalent to 970 Btu per lb of water at 212 degrees F.

To raise surface water at 62 degrees F to 212 degrees will require 150 Btu per lb (1 Btu per degree per lb).

To superheat this 212-degree steam to 1,600 degrees F will require [22] about 700 Btu per lb of water (0.5 Btu per lb per degree F). Steam as used, then, will require about 1,800 Btu per lb of water equivalent. At 350 lb per bbl of water, 630 thousand Btu will be required to turn this water into superheated steam at 1,600 degrees F.

If the coal-to-boiler-to-steam cycle is 80% efficient, 630 thousand Btu will require 0.035 tons of coal averaging 22.4 million Btu per ton. At a weighted average of $30 per ton of coal, a bbl of water can be converted into superheated steam at a cost of just over $1 a bbl.

The *Scientific Encyclopedia* [22], Exxon [54] and others agree that 2 to 3 bbl of water per bbl of syncrude may be required for process steam. If we accept this, then it is evident that the steam-cost per bbl of syncrude will be somewhat less than $3 per bbl.

T. E. Edgar and J. T. Richardson [64] state that a 250-million-cu-ft-a-day SNG plant will consume 2.8 million gallons of water per day as steam and will need 21 million gallons for cooling. Cooling-water is cheap, but we have opted for a continuous-growth economy and the competition for water is fierce.

Such a plant would consume 67,000 bbl of water a day (as steam) for the production of 250 thousand Mcf of SNG, a ratio of 0.268 bbl per Mcf. At a conversion cost of "just over $1 a bbl," for water-to-superheated-steam, the steam cost would be 25 to 30¢ per Mcf of SNG.

THE USE OF OXYGEN

Both hydrogen and oxygen for the dozens of synthetic processes now in various stages of development can be produced from the electrolysis of water: $2H_2O = 2H_2 + O_2$, but "the economics are unfavorable" [22].

If as stated by the *Scientific Encyclopedia* [22], a large-scale 240 Mw(e) plant is required to produce 40,000 Mcf of hydrogen per day, the plant would presumably be coal-fired. Such a plant, at 3,410 Btu per hour per kilowatt [65], would require a net of 19.64 billion Btu per day. At 40% efficiency for a coal-fired electric plant, 49.1 billion gross Btu per day would be needed.

At a weighted average of $30 per ton for coal of 22.4 million Btu per ton, 40,000 Mcf per day of hydrogen would cost about $1.65 per Mcf. Giving credit for the by-product oxygen, hydrogen from the electrolysis of water would still cost about $1.10 per Mcf and oxygen about 55¢.

These costs do seem to be high. The modern oxygen plants designed as integral parts of synthetic-fuel plants are lox plants, manufacturing oxygen by the fractional distillation of liquid air [31]. I cannot find in the literature any specific unit costs in 1980 dollars, but to beat the cost of electrolysis it should be below 40 or 50¢ per Mcf.

Specific estimates of oxygen usage in a multitude of processes, using fuels that vary all the way from lignites to high-Btu bituminous coals, show a variation from less than 4 to more than 16 Mcf of oxygen per ton of coal. At a weighted average, about 7.5 Mcf of oxygen per ton of coal will be required for the production of either SNG or syncrude. At 15 Mcf of SNG or 2.35 bbl of syncrude per ton of coal, the cost of oxygen should be 20 to 25¢ per Mcf of gas, and somewhat less than $2.00 per bbl of oil.

Hydrocarbons from coal, whatever the process used, require the chemical reaction of hydrogen and carbon under controlled conditions. The simplest reaction is: $C + 2H_2 = CH_4$ (methane), but the commercial processes developed over the past 20 years have become more complex than this in order to be cost-effective. Water, as superheated steam, is now the universal source of the hydrogen atom. In the cost analyses set out above, this steam-cost is specifically stated.

In the production of SNG from coal, most of the processes call for a high-temperature reaction with steam and oxygen. The oxygen reacts with part of the coal to raise the temperature of this endothermic process high enough for the rest of the coal to react rapidly with steam to produce a low-Btu synthesis gas composed of CO and H_2, plus some methane. Complete methanation can be achieved in a nickel-catalyst converter by a shift in the atomic arrangements of the synthesis gas: $2CO + 2H_2 = CH_4 + CO_2$. The CO_2 is then scrubbed out. Many specific SNG processes have been developed, but we have not computed a hydrogen cost for any of these, for this cost is included in the estimated cost of the superheated steam.

THE USE OF HYDROGEN

The production of syncrude from coal involves more complicated processes and uses more hydrogen per unit of product; but here again no hydrogen cost is added, for the hydrogen atom comes from steam and the unit-cost for this steam has already been included.

Part of the additional hydrogen required can be obtained by treating the CO part of synthesis gas with more steam: $CO + H_2O = H_2 + CO_2$. After scrubbing out the CO_2, the synthesis gas is all hydrogen, ready for syncrude production.

In syncrude processes involving pyrolysis of the coal (anaerobic distillation producing char, tar and gas) a portion of the gas product can be reformed into hydrogen.

Hydrogen can also be supplied from a gasifier using pyrolysis residues, steam, oxygen and more coal if necessary.

11

Total Costs of
Synfuels From Coal

So we come at last to the bottom line: what will it cost us to put synthetic fuels, made from coal, into the pipeline? There are very few published estimates, and none of them are from authoritative sources. The standard comment in the press is "we don't know" or "no one can be sure" [55]. Well I am sure, within reasonable limits, and so are the technical personnel of at least three dozen corporations who have plans to make synthetic fuels.

The bottom line is plain and simple: *we can make synthetic fuels from U.S. coals cheaper than we can import oil and gas.*

SYNCRUDE COSTS

If we accept the weighted-average coal-cost of $13 per bbl of syncrude, plant amortization costs of $4 per bbl, operating costs of $2 and the above accessory costs of $5 for oxygen and steam, then synthetic crude oil can be made from a weighted average of U.S. coals for about $25 per bbl in 1981 dollars. Inflation may raise this price; but if it does it will also raise the price of competitive imports, so we are perfectly justified in say-ing that we have a bargain, that an estimated $25 syn-crude in 1981 makes an important hedge against OPEC's 1981 price of $35.

Insofar as I know, there are no published authoritative estimates of costs per bbl for synthetic liquids made from U.S. oil shales and tar sands or from renewable biomass, but the costs will certainly be of the same order of magnitude. Large-scale retorting of oil shales *in situ* should cost even less, if pilot-plant data can be reliably extrapolated.

All of this should be welcome news, but our Administration in Washington shows no sense of urgency in the development of a synfuels program; they have, in fact, downgraded it from its 1980 status in our plans. Yet those who know the oil business, and live by it, are certain that there is no reasonable limit to OPEC oil prices unless the importing industrial nations develop alternative fuel sources with all possible diligence [66]. Even Exxon, expecting to find every drop of domestic oil its budget will permit, expects U.S. crude oil production to drop 40% in the next 20 years [25].

To be blunt, it is we, not OPEC, who should set oil prices for this country. "We know what it costs us to make it, and that will be the ceiling price for imported crude" is the only workable answer to projected OPEC price hikes.

SNG COSTS

If we accept our weighted-average estimate of a $2 coal-cost per Mcf of SNG, a plant amortization cost of 45¢, operating costs of 15¢ and the above accessory costs of 50¢ for steam and oxygen, then synthetic natural gas can be produced from a weighted average of U.S. coals for about $3.10 per Mcf.

This is above the FPC's interstate ceiling price (which may soon be removed) but is well below the $4.47 per Mcf we pay in 1981 for natural gas imported from Canada and from Mexico. Here again, within a decade we could set a ceiling on import prices by our diligence in making synthetics from our own natural resources. Will we?

12

Ecology, Geography and Synthesis

"Synfuels are here," in the rhetorical sense; but they are not here, not anywhere, in the physical sense. Nor will they be until our energy corporations build the necessary plants, with capital accumulated out of profits.

Politico-corporate relationships are beyond my competence, but this much I do know: only our oil, gas, electric utility and mining companies have the muscle, the know-how and the organizations to produce synthetic fuels from our coals and from other sources. They also know that all such plants must reach forward into the future for 30 to 40 years to recover the enormous capital investment required.

It makes no sense in this corporate-oriented era to put the federal government into the synfuels business; but we do have Bureaus, Agencies and Departments that can be of enormous help by bringing their expertise to bear on the problems these corporations will face.

STRIP MINING

These problems are many and the decisions will be difficult, but the plants will be built. In making viable decisions involving a necessary balance between corporate profits and ecological acceptability, these data are pertinent:

The cheapest coal is strip-mined coal, as evidenced by the fact that in 1980 about 60% of our commercial coal came from strip mines [20], though we have estimated that not more than 14% of our recoverable coal can ultimately be surface-mined. In judging among the U.S. coals for synfuel raw materials, bear in mind that:

Approximately 20 billion tons in the East and the Southeast are shallow enough to strip, and the coal is of the highest quality; but a great deal of this lies in the hills of Appalachia and *this must not be stripped,* for the ecology of the region will not stand it. The proof is there for all to see, for far too much has already been stripped.

For more than 50 years, coal has been strip-mined from the Midwestern coal fields. Much of the older work left behind a battle-scarred landscape, but we do not have to permit this. In flat country where rainfall is sufficient, the coal can be strip-mined and the land acceptably restored [4, p. 110], though our new Interior Secretary is not inclined to demand this.

Most of this coal has a sulfur content of 3–4%, but this is no detriment in synfuels processes. For the long-term public weal it is this coal, plus ecologically acceptable high-sulfur coal from the East and the Southeast, which is most expendable [4, p. 97] in our long-term plans.

Both of these areas offer all of the other raw materials necessary for syncrude and SNG plants using any one of a dozen methods. Energy-company executives will find these techniques in various stages of development:

SYNFUEL PROCESSES

1. The only commercial syncrude process in operation today (SASOL) involves the retorting of coal with both oxygen and steam. The oxygen is made from air by liquefaction and fractional distillation. Costs are nominal for liquid oxygen (lox) plants in this area and water, the indispensable item, is presumably readily available [9, 22].

2. The only commercial SNG process in operation today also involves the treatment of coal with oxygen and steam by a specific process [49] developed by Lurgi in the 1930s.

3. The Bureau of Mines [4, p. 109] has developed through the pilot stage a high-pressure process (SYNTHOIL) to convert high-sulfur-coal to low-sulfur oil by heating it with hydrogen in a fuel-oil medium. It sounds waterless, but in this era affordable hydrogen will have to come from water via superheated steam, using processes previously described.

4. The Bureau has achieved the same success at high pressures using coal + CO + steam. One assumes that part of the coal furnishes the CO.

5. Many syncrude processes developed through the pilot-plant stage start with the pyrolysis of coal (heated in an airless retort) at low pressures to produce char, tar and a gas product. All of the gas and about a third of the char can be used to sustain the temperature required for retorting, leaving the operator with $2/3$ of the char and all of the tar; or the necessary heat can be supplied by

burning coal under the retort, leaving the operator with the gas as well as all of the char and all of the tar. From this beginning can come a variety of endings, dictated by geography, ecology and economics.

In the arid West, the lignites and the subbituminous coals will give off about 1.7 bbl of water per ton of coal when heated. This would be usable to make some steam to make some hydrogen to make some syncrude. If coal is burned under the retort, then the pyrolysis gas can be reformed to furnish more hydrogen. But we are still up against an ecological no-no in the arid Western states: there is not enough *renewable* water to complete the desired reactions and also furnish water for cooling. If the operator wishes to use *nonrenewable* water and is permitted to do so, then syncrude and SNG can be made from Western coals as long as the water holds out.

If the process is stopped short of complete crude-oil synthesis, the char is an excellent fuel as well as a source of synthetics. It can be shipped East for either purpose; or it can be used in the arid West as the perfect fuel for a waterless magnetohydrodynamic generator [4, p. 102]. The tar can be sent East for conversion to syncrude or for use as a source of petrochemicals to replace the current feedstocks of oil or gas.

6. A process known as COED (Clear-Oil-Energy-Development-Project) has successfully passed the pilot-plant stage and is ready for demonstration. Crushed and dried coal is subjected to pyrolysis in 4 successive stages at temperatures of 600, 800, 1,000 and 1,600 degrees F. Some of the gas from a continuing process is used to heat the retort in stage 1. The succeeding stages 2, 3 and 4 are

heated by the combusion of process char and by the exothermal gasification reaction produced in stage 4 by the introduction of oxygen and steam. In the final reaction in stage 4, coal is "converted to synthetic crude oil and other clean fuels" [22].

7. The Office of Coal Research (OCR) supported the Consolidation Coal Co. in the development of THE CO_2 ACCEPTOR PROCESS [49] which achieves gasification of coal by an ingenious series of steps requiring the usual superheated steam but avoiding the necessity for oxygen:

An "acceptor," limestone or dolomite, is calcined (oxidized) in a separate reactor by burning coal in air under the retort. One of the combustion products is CO_2. Heat for the gasification process is then supplied by the exothermic reaction of the calcined "acceptor" with the CO_2 ($CaO + CO_2 = CaCO_3$) to produce again the original carbonate from the oxide [22]. The necessity for an oxygen plant is avoided, yet no nitrogenous gases are introduced into the final SNG. The heat supplied by the "acceptor" reaction is enough to sustain a high-temperature high-pressure carbon-steam reaction producing a raw gas containing carbon monoxide (CO), hydrogen (H_2) and some methane (CH_4). The raw gas goes then for an extensive clean-up in a gas-purification plant and from there to the catalytic shift converter, where it is reformed into methane. The final product is pipeline quality SNG.

8. A promising low-pressure process, COGAS, for the conversion of coal to gas and oil products, takes advantage of the high efficiency of multistage coal pyrolysis and the reactivity of steam with the pyrolysis char [22].

Both SNG and syncrude can be produced by this process. (a) The pyrolysis gas goes through what catalytic conversion (methanation) may be necessary enroute to the gas purification plant and thence to the SNG pipeline. (b) The hot char is subjected to gasification with steam and air in a "hot burden" process (unexplained) "without introduction of nitrogen from the air into the synthesis gas" [22]. (c) A part of this synthesis gas becomes SNG after going through the catalytic shift converter and the gas purification plant. (d) The rest of the gas is reformed to produce hydrogen, and this is used for the hydrogenation of the pyrolysis tar into a medium-heavy fuel oil or into synthetic crude oil.

COGAS Development Co. expects that commercial plants using this process will be built in the decade of the 1980s.

9. The HYGAS process [49] was developed by the Institute of Gas Technology (IGT) from studies which began as early as 1944. It was soon learned that coal will react with oxygen and steam to form synthesis gas ($CO + H_2$) which can be shifted to methane by techniques now widely known. From this it was an easy step to: CO plus more steam will yield $H_2 + CO_2$, making it possible to come out with a clean hydrogen product from coal gasification.

As presently designed, part of the coal is gasified and the synthesis gas shifted over to hydrogen. The char and the rest of the coal are subjected to direct hydrogenation at high temperatures and pressures to produce a gas which is largely methane. A final methanation reaction yields SNG of pipeline quality.

10. Bituminous Coal Research, Inc. with help from the OCR has ready still another SNG process, BY-GAS [22], a 2-stage gasifier in which coal in the second stage is treated with the hot synthesis gas produced in stage 1 by the usual process, coal plus steam and oxygen. The stage 2 product is methane plus more synthesis gas. The customary catalytic converter and the gas purification plant will produce SNG ready for the pipeline.

11. The HYDRANE process is based upon the 2-stage hydrogasifier concept developed by the U.S. Bureau of Mines [22]. The objective is to gasify any raw coal or pyrolysis char directly to methane by contact-reaction with hydrogen.

The hydrogen is made in a separate plant by the reaction of char with oxygen and an excess of steam, in a process similar to those previously described.

Into the coal in the bottom stage there is introduced 16 cu ft of hydrogen per lb of dry coal. The hydrogen-coal reaction, consisting of pyrolysis and hydrogasification, starts at about 750 degrees F and proceeds rapidly at higher temperatures. The yield of 10 cu ft per lb of dry coal is almost totally methane. If a high-Btu bituminous coal is used (28 million Btu per ton) then the indicated thermal efficiency is 70%, which places this method high on the list of pilot-tested commercial possibilities.

12. In 1974 the U.S. Bureau of Mines completed a pilot-plant study of its SYNTHANE process [49] and began operating a demonstration plant near Pittsburgh.

Coal is pretreated to destroy its caking properties, car-

bonized in the first stage of the gasifier and then gasified with steam and oxygen in the second stage. After a
shift conversion to yield a hydrogen-to-carbon monoxide
ratio of 3:1, the gas is methanated in a nickel-catalyst
converter.

In late 1979 the DOE announced that the plant would
be shut down on December first for lack of funds, but
it is to be hoped that new synfuels funds will be found
to permit it to function as a demonstration unit.

13. The Consol Synthetic Fuel Process consists of the
    partial conversion of coal into an extract and a
    by-product solid residue, followed by hydrogena-
    tion of the extract to yield syncrude. The hydro-
    gen is made by "commercially proven methods"
    [22] such as those previously described.

DIFFERENCES AND DISTINCTIONS

Basically, all of the processes described above are the
same: all synfuels made from coal are hydrocarbons and
these must be made in some manner by combining carbon from coal with hydrogen from water. The differences,
and they are many, are in the engineering techniques
[49]: the method of supplying heat for the gasification or liquefaction reaction; the method of achieving
contact between the reactants; the flow of reactants,
with or against the flow of the coal, char or tar; the
choice of the reactant or reactants, hydrogen or steam-
plus-oxygen; and the type and condition of the residues
to be disposed of or converted to useful substances. All
of the above-described processes are through the pilot-
plant stage and quite a few have successfully operated

at the demonstration-plant level. Choices must be made by the technical and executive personnel of the corporations who decide to invest their billions in commercial plants. These decisions will be influenced to some extent by the specific preferences of those who decide where federal synfuels money will be spent.

THE ARID WEST

Of our recoverable near-surface coal, 75% is in thick easy-to-strip beds in our arid Western states. But *this is not the place* for our synfuel plants, for 2 to 3 bbl of water are required to make a bbl of syncrude [54] and the West has no water to spare. Where hydrogen is required, it has to be made from part of that water [22]; steam comes from the same source and some water is required for cooling. Oxygen is no problem, here or elsewhere, for it is easily made by the selective distillation of liquefied air.

A definitive study of the situation was completed on October 15, 1973, by a Study Committee of the National Academy of Sciences (NAS):

"The shortage of water," says the Committee, "is a major factor in planning for future development of coal reserves in the American West." In most areas, they conclude, there is enough water for strip-mining the coal and restoring the land, but that is all. Unless we are willing to concede that the ground waters and the drainage basins of the Rocky Mountain states and the Northern Great Plains are expendable, there is not enough water for mine-mouth steam-electric plants or for synfuel plants to convert coal to oil or gas [67, pp. 456-458].

In the driest areas, notably the Four Corners area of Utah, Colorado, Arizona and New Mexico, there is not, and never will be, enough water to strip-mine the land and then rehabilitate it. In such areas, says the Committee, we must leave the coal or honestly acknowledge that we are creating deserts by our environmental degradation [67, pp. 456-458].

So we create deserts. Right now one of the largest strip-mine steam-electric power plants in the world is in full operation in the Four Corners area and several more of them are planned, using ground water from 3800 feet deep. A lot of money will be made there, but we who pay the price will have paid too dearly.

Water could be imported to the Western states at considerable cost, and ecologically acceptable systems could be constructed; but I find no evidence to indicate that our energy corporations have any such plans. On the contrary, they have been moving heavily into the arid Western coal fields with the overt cooperation of our own Interior Department's Bureau of Reclamation, and there is every indication that this is where they plan their major expansion.

I don't know just where the clout exists, if it does exist, to compel our energy corporations to restrict their operations to ecologically acceptable areas; but if anything at all can be done, the time is now, for a large part of the master-plan water rights and mining rights were secured during the decade of the 1970s [67, pp. 456-458].

I cannot say what changes in plans have been made since that time, but certainly there is more awareness on the part of our energy corporations that their actions may be subject to intensive public scrutiny. The day of the Environmental Impact Study is with us; and at the corporate executive level increasing consideration is being given to the value of a good public image. Enlightened self-interest is also at work, for most of our major energy corporations now have *Synthetic Fuels Divisions* staffed by persons who comprehend the long-term technical problems and are also aware of the extent to which their action may or may not be in the public interest. Let us be hopeful that their actions will reflect their comprehension.

Meanwhile synfuels plants of pilot, demonstration or commercial size are now under construction or under consideration in California, Pennsylvania, Eastern Kentucky, Western Kentucky, West Virginia, Virginia, Texas, New Mexico, Wyoming, North Dakota, Illinois and Colorado.

IN SITU GASIFICATION

Synthetic Natural Gas from the underground gasification of coal (*in situ*) has long been under consideration by several government Bureaus and Agencies and by numerous energy corporations; but in past decades there has been no economic incentive to develop the pilot-plant techniques which must precede the design and construction of commercial plants.

Ten years ago the gas produced would have been in competition with abundant interstate natural gas priced at 35¢ per Mcf. In the decades ahead, the comparison will be with SNG at $3.10 or more per Mcf, and gas produced from coal *in situ* should easily meet this competitive price.

In our first comparative test, the energy-conversion efficiency, the data available are rather fuzzy. As far back as 1971 the Bureau of Mines stated that "Underground gasification of coal is technically feasible. . . . The development of full-scale commercial techniques could provide, even from high-sulfur coals, a clean low-Btu gas and eliminate some of the safety, health, and environmental problems associated with coal mining" [20].

E. F. Osborn, who ran the first tests, using air as an oxidizing agent, reports that the "energy conversion efficiency is quite high"; but it is difficult to share his opinion, since his "continuous flow of gas" was composed of 5% methane, 10% carbon monoxide, 15% hydrogen, 15% carbon dioxide and 55% oxides of nitrogen.

Harry Perry, the Bureau's director of coal research for many years, expressed the same doubts of these early experiments [49], stating that most underground gasification tests to that date (early 1974) had resulted in poor recovery of the energy and chemical values of the coal.

To push things along, Philip H. Abelson of *Science* suggested that since the technology for producing oxygen (from air) has become efficient and cheap, oxygen should be used in place of air as the oxidant. Even with high-sulfur coals, the result would certainly be a richer gas, for it would contain almost no nitrogen oxides. After the carbon dioxide and hydrogen sulfide are scrubbed out, the gas should consist almost entirely of the combustibles hydrogen, carbon monoxide and methane.

In recent years oxygen and oxygen-plus-steam processes have been used successfuly in pilot-plant gasification of coal *in situ*, with reported energy-conversion efficiencies of 50 to 80%. As a basis for economic comparison, the upper and lower limits of thermal efficiency for strip-mined or shaft-mined coals processed into SNG are as follows:

If the standard American room-and-pillar under-ground mining methods are used, only about 50% of the coal-in-place will be recovered. If an average 60% of the energy content is converted to SNG, then 60% of 50% or 30% of the energy-in-place will be recovered in SNG plants.

At the other end of the spectrum, strip mines should recover 80 to 85% of the surface coal available. If our SNG processes should be brought up to 70% efficiency, then our ultimate limit on the recovery of the energy-in-place would be 70% of 85% or about 60% for strip-mined coal processed in synthetic natural gas plants.

It is probable that the efficiency of *in situ* gasifica-tion lies in between, at about 40%, though some esti-mates place it higher. It has this ultimate disadvantage: 40-odd trace elements available from coal are left for-ever in the ground; but it has this distinct advantage: gas not otherwise available can be recovered efficiently from coal beds that are too thin, too thick, too deep or too steep to mine. In addition to these, we have more than 400 billion tons of lignite beds whose energy con-tent is 6,000 to 7,400 Btu per lb and thus are presently noncompetitive as shaft-mined coal. Also, some coals suitable for *in situ* gasification are too dangerous to mine because of underground structural weaknesses.

Specifically [22], in areas where water of any quality is readily available, the underground gasification of coal can be accomplished successfully by fracturing the coal beds and injecting oxygen and steam under pressure into the fractured areas. Drawn off for further processing into SNG or liquid fuels are the combustibles methane, carbon monoxide and hydrogen. Also present are carbon dioxide, and hydrogen sulfide if the coal contains sul-fur, but these can be scrubbed out to send a clean prod-uct from the gas-treatment plant.

In this surface facility the combustibles, by appropriate treatment, can be re-formed into any product desired. Also required are an oxygen plant and a steam plant (any old water will do). The ecological impact would seem to be low and the costs moderate.

More recently, Gulf Oil Corporation, with the help of $13.5 million from DOE, has completed a successful semi-combustion pilot project using oxygen to partially burn a steeply dipping coal seam at Rawlings, Wyoming [30].

Pairs of wells were drilled into the coal seam. In one well of each pair the coal was set afire in an oxygen atmosphere, and from the other well there was extracted a nitrogen-free low-Btu synthesis gas. In areas where water is plentiful, this gas could make an excellent fuel for steam-electric power plants (see our previous discussion of the renewed use of small, low-Btu gasifiers). With the application of the proper techniques, the gases from this process and from other *in situ* processes could be used to produce SNG or liquid fuels [30].

Gulf reports that "the competitive economics are good," but they don't state their basis of comparison. Considering the enormous capital costs of opening new coal mines and building synfuel plants, I am prepared to believe that "the economics are good" in comparison with almost any known process for extracting synfuels. From the meager data the operator gives, it is still possible to judge that the energy-conversion efficiency of *in situ* gasification by partial combustion with oxygen will be about 40%.

It should be borne in mind that successful underground gasification projects would add substantially to the tonnage of coal that we now class as recoverable. It would also speed up our synfuels program, for it seems certain that *in situ* projects could be completed in much less time than the anticipated 6 to 8 years for coal mines plus synfuel conversion plants. It is also possible that some projected coal mines would not need to be opened because of the energy supplied by large-scale *in situ* gasification projects.

GASOHOL

In spite of the current fanfare over gasohol, the production and use of ethyl alcohol made by the fermentation and distillation of agricultural products doesn't have a high efficiency rating in petroleum conservation. In U.S. agribusiness, it now takes the equivalent of a gallon of gasoline (in fuel, chemical fertilizers and pesticides) to raise a bushel of corn [67, p. 448]. That bushel can be converted by fermentation and distillation into an average of 2.8 gallons of ethanol, with a Btu content equal to 2 gallons of gasoline [68, pp. 56,69].

However, there is some gain in a 2 to 1 swap, and scientists at Southern Illinois University are about ready to publish the initial results of their EthaCoal research, which indicate that this gain can be stretched still farther [69].

Following up the initial work by the Keller Corporation of Dallas, Texas, these scientists seem to have developed a successful marriage of ethanol and high-sulfur coal [69]. In a high-pressure high-temperature retort, the mixture is partially burned to a point at which an enriched liquid separates from the solid components and the sulfur goes off as sulfur dioxide. The residue of char is a clean-burning fuel, and the liquid has similar characteristics to diesel fuel.

Here again, there is an energy loss in the combustion of part of the material to sustain the process, but EthaCoal is certainly worth following up. As their experiments continue, I suggest that methanol might take the place of ethanol. I cannot see that there is any important molecular difference, and we can produce methanol in considerable volume without the use of petroleum or petroleum products—a substantial gain in the area of our greatest concern [68, pp. 63,67,69].

COAL DEGASIFICATION

Though not, strictly speaking, a synthetic fuel, the trillions of cu ft of methane indigenous to the coal beds of the U.S. are a great danger in the mining of the coal but would be an asset if the gas could be recovered in advance of mining [62]. E. F. Osborn of the U.S. Bureau of Mines stated in 1971 that a promising technique indicates that this may be practical; but I have heard nothing of it since that time, except for this 1974 comment in *Science.*

COAL SOLVENTS

The products of coal-solvent processes are synthetic fuels in the sense that they do not occur in nature, but it is too early to estimate just what part they will play in lessening our consumption of petroleum products.

The Southern Company [63] dissolves coal with a recoverable chemical solvent, filters it to remove impurities, and then resolidifies it. The result: a clean fuel with little sulfur or ash and a very high unit-heat value.

Combustion Engineering, Inc. is also developing a "solvent refining process" which de-sulfurs and de-ashes coal into a clean-burning liquid fuel.

The Battelle Memorial Institute [70] has successfully completed the laboratory studies of a pre-combustion "hydrothermal process" that removes most of the sulfur in elemental (commercial) form and can extract and purify potentially valuable trace metals and coal chemicals. In my opinion, future generations will find this a valuable addition to our options.

Gulf Oil Corporation in cooperation with the DOE is working to develop a liquid coal that could be a practical substitute for some petroleum products [30]. Unlike some of the other solvent-refined coals, the end product is a liquid. It can be transported by pipeline and burned under steam boilers in the same manner as fuel oil. As with similar processes, the product is free of ash and very low in sulfur. Gulf reports that during a week's test under Consolidated Edison's boilers, Solvent Refined Coal II, as they call it, was quite successful.

After 2 years of negotiations, the first "$1.4 to $1.5 billion plant to demonstrate the technology on a commercial scale" was supposed to be a joint venture of Gulf's Pittsburgh Midway Coal Mining Company, the governments of Japan and West Germany, and the DOE [71]. Right now, however, the ambivalence of the new Administration toward all synfuel ventures has placed this project in serious jeopardy. The Japanese are "outraged" and the West Germans are "reconsidering."

13

Our Future

The preceding pages were originally written as PART II of a proposed 1981 revision of my 1975 book *Fuels, Minerals and Human Survival*. But when I became convinced that we would indeed have a Coal Era, I could not stop there: I had to know just what can be done throughout the energy spectrum by the time the Petroleum Era is finished. Figures 3, 4, 5 and 7 supply the answers I am able to give.

We will certainly be in the middle of the Coal Era by the year 2060. U.S. production of this fuel is expected to increase by 350% (Figure 2). Of the total production, about 50% will be burned as primary fuel; somewhat less than 20% will be exported; and we expect to send more than 30% to our then-installed synfuel plants (Figure 3).

If our calculations are correct, we will be able to hold our supply of petroleum liquids up to 70% of 1980 levels (Figure 4) by the addition of synthetic crudes made from biomass, from coal and from oil shales and tar sands. But unless underground gasification becomes an important source of SNG, our supply of gas may be somewhat less than 70% of 1980. Gas consumption could fall below 50% of 1980 levels (Figure 5).

Our greatest problem within this time frame will be

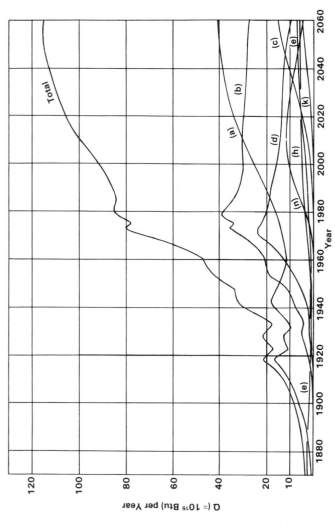

Figure 7. Projected U.S. energy consumption. (a) Coal; (b) petroleum liquids; (c) solar [5]; (d) gas; (e) biomass as fuel [7]; (h) hydroelectric; (k) geothermal [72]; (n) nuclear [4, p. 21].

the acquisition of the metals and minerals to make the hardware.

Of the 36 metals and minerals considered necessary to maintain our industrial economy [73] we import 75 to 100% of 15 of these, 25 to 75% of another 13, and less than 25% of the remaining 8. Even if politics and economics permit us to continue to use more than our fair share of these materials, world supplies are deteriorating rapidly [4]. Within two decades, the world-wide demand will exceed the world-wide supply for more than 20 critical metals and minerals. By 2050 the increasing shortfall will extend to more than 30 vital materials.

From the abundant literature on energy sources, both sound and fanciful, I have brought together in Figure 7 my best estimates of the rise and/or fall of all the energy sources now in use or under discussion:

1. nuclear;
2. geothermal;
3. hydroelectric;
4. wood, wastes and other biomass burned as fuel or processed into synthetic fuels;
5. gas, both natural and synthetic;
6. solar power of many kinds;
7. petroleum liquids from all known sources; and
8. coal burned as a primary fuel.

If we are able to meet these estimates, then we will be able to continue an increasing usage of energy as the Petroleum Era fades out, but the increase will be minor in comparison to the Era of Petroleum.

During the 40 years from 1933 to 1973, our total energy usage increased by about 350% (Figure 7). From that point on, the most that we can expect is an increase of less than 50% in the 80 years to follow.

THE GROWTH CONCEPT

The reader may wonder how a government dedicated to a continuous-growth economy, "in a world (where) hopes for further economic growth cannot be realized" [74], can deal with this problem during a period when our population (natives, immigrants and illegals) will more than double [75]. I invite him to wonder [4, p. 158], but I cannot answer him.

Acceptable answers, in fact, are hard to come by. The most prestigious studies of the last decade were made by the Harvard Business School, the Ford Foundation and Resources for the Future. In reviewing these works collectively, *Science* [76] suggests that the studies are "deeply pessimistic," since not one of them holds out any real hope that we will take the actions needed to solve our energy problems.

One wonders, indeed, in this year 1981 if our fundamental planner, the federal government, even acknowledges that such problems exist.

Glossary

AGA: the American Gas Association.

anaerobic: no air present.

anthracite coals: very low in volatile matter and moisture. Heat content varies from 13,500 to 15,000 Btu per lb.

"bank mines": the "cottage industries" of the coal business. Local enterprises generally working through tunnels driven back into the hills on coal outcrops.

bbl: barrel or barrels, depending on the context.

billion: used in the American sense of 1,000 million.

biomass: renewable organic material which came into being as a result of biological growth or metabolism. In its broadest sense, it also includes any manufactured organic material and some of the wastes from such processes.

bituminous coals: heat content varies from 12,000 to 15,400 Btu per lb.

Btu: a British thermal unit, defined as the energy necessary to raise the temperature of one lb of water one degree Fahrenheit.

C: centigrade or Celsius. A measurement of temperature wherein water freezes at zero degrees and boils at 100, with the difference divided into 100 parts.

catalyst: any material which causes activity between two or more substances without itself being affected.

catalytic converter: a device for shifting atoms from a less desirable to a more desirable molecular structure. Specifically, under the influence of a nickel catalyst in the converter, producer gas from coal can be shifted over into SNG, as described in the preceding pages. The converter must be operated under optimum conditions, for the impurities in some synthesis gas are injurious to the catalyst.

char: the carbon residue from the pyrolysis of coal. It is quite similar to both charcoal and metallurgical coke.

cu ft: cubic foot or cubic feet, depending on the context.

de facto: actually existing, from whatever cause or for whatever reason.

demonstration plant: as the term implies, this plant, processing 1000 or more tons per day, is designed to demonstrate that a particular method will succeed commercially. Many millions are spent to justify the spending of billions.

DOE: the Department of Energy, targeted for abolition [18].

ecology: a science dedicated to the harmony of people and their environment, in a manner designed to preserve the well-being of both in perpetuity.

endothermic: requiring heat.

ethanol: our drinking alcohol; the active ingredient in all alcoholic beverages.

exothermic: giving off heat.

F: Fahrenheit. A temperature measurement in which water freezes at 32 degrees and boils at 212 with the difference divided into 180 parts.

FERC: the Federal Energy Regulatory Commission.

FPC: the Federal Power Commission.

gasifier: a complete small plant for converting coal to synthesis gas.

gasohol: a mixture of gasoline with either ethyl or methyl alcohol. At 5 to 10% alcohol, only minor adjustments to the automobile's carburetor are necessary. With major adjustments, 20% alcohol works quite well. The motors can, in fact, be adjusted to run on 100% alcohol.

geothermal: literally, heat from the earth. Natural steam vents, hot waters under pressure which can be reached by drilling, and areas of very hot dry rocks at reasonable depths will all furnish useful enregy in the short-term future.

ground water: water that flows or is pumped from porous formations below ground level. Some is renewable; some is not.

hydrogasification: converting coal to gas by the use of hydrogen.

hydrogenation: to combine with hydrogen.

IGT: the Institute of Gas Technology.

in situ: literally, " in its original place". As used herein, it refers to the recovery of oil or gas from shale or coal without mining the source material.

kilowatt: a thousand watts.

lb: a pound, or pounds, depending on the context.

lignites: sometimes known as "brown coal". The heat content varies from 6,000 to 7,400 Btu per lb in the United States.

LMFBR: a liquid-metal-cooled fast-breeder nuclear reactor. In essence, a nuclear power plant which converts otherwise unusable forms of uranium and/or thorium into useful fuels, while supplying a net output of power as efficiently as the reactors in current use.

lox: liquid oxygen.

LWR: a light-water-cooled nuclear reactor. This distinction is made (light water being ordinary water) because of the fact that "heavy water" reactors have been built. In this rare variety of water, the hydrogen is replaced by deuterium, a hydrogen of twice the mass of ordinary hydrogen.

magnetohydrodynamic generator: a new method of drawing electricity from fast-flowing hot gases. The fuel, char for example, is burned at very high temperatures and the gaseous products of combustion are made electrically conductive by salting the gas with potassium carbonate. This ionized gas then travels at supersonic speed through a magnetic field and creates a flow of direct current. Thermal efficiency can reach 60%. The system is waterless.

Mcf: a thousand cu ft, the standard measurement for natural gas.

methanation: conversion to methane.

methane: the main ingredient of natural gas. Chemically, CH_4.

methanol: our old stand-by, wood alcohol.

Mw(e): literally, a million watts of electrical output. The explanatory (e) is always added to signify usable output, for all plants are less than 100% efficient and the (gross) power input always exceeds the (net) power output.

NAS: the National Academy of Sciences.

NRC: the Nuclear Regulatory Commission, a new portion of the old AEC, the Atomic Energy Commission.

nuclear fusion: the thermonuclear reaction which powers our sun. Under optimum conditions, two nuclei of some very light atoms will fuse together, forming one heavier nucleus and giving up mass as energy.

OCR: the Office of Coal Research.

oil equivalent: an Mcf of natural gas contains about a million Btu and a bbl of crude oil about 5.7 million. On this basis, 5.7 Mcf of gas is equivalent to a bbl of oil.

OPEC: the Organization of Petroleum Exporting Countries, a cartel which sets world oil prices.

overt: not concealed or secret.

photovoltaic cell: a specific device which produces electricity when sunlight falls on it. Also known as a photoelectric cell.

pilot plant: the next step beyond the laboratory test of a method or process. In synfuel terms, this generally means the processing of 50 to 100 tons of coal or oil shales or tar sands per day.

pyrolysis: the subjection of organic compounds to high temperatures in closed vessels (retorts) in the absence of air. The resulting decomposition yields products which can be converted into a variety of useful substances by a variety of processes.

Q: a quadrillion Btu ($= 10^{15}$ Btu).

reactants: the materials which are brought together to form other substances by chemical reactions.

SASOL process: the syncrude process used in the Union of South Africa. The exact engineering techniques are kept secret, but the basic process consists of retorting coal with both oxygen and steam.

scrubber: any one of several devices designed to remove sulfur from coal as it is burned. At 3 to 4% sulfur content, about 70 lb per ton of coal can be recovered as a commercial product. On the current market [77] where sulfur is in very short supply, 70 lb is worth about $4, which will go a long way toward paying the cost of scrubbing.

short ton: the customary U.S. ton of 2,000 lb. Also used are long tons, 2240 lb, and metric tons, 2205 lb.

SNG: synthetic natural gas: It must meet the general requirement of about 1000 Btu per cu ft.

status quo: the existing state or condition.

strip mining: the recovery of coal at or near the surface by mechanical equipment.

subbituminous coals: soft coals with about 25% moisture and a heat content of 8,600 to 10,900 Btu per lb.

syncrude: synthetic crude oil from coal, oil shales or tar sands. From coal, the product is about equal to natural crude at 5.7 million Btu per bbl. From oil shales, the product runs about 5.4 million Btu per bbl. Bitumen from tar sands is upgraded to produce an oil of poor quality which is difficult to define [31].

synfuels: fuels not found in nature, but manufactured from naturally occurring organic materials.

synthesis gas: a synonym for producer gas, the commonest product of the treatment of coal with steam and oxygen. It is composed largely of carbon monoxide (CO) and hydrogen (H_2) with a small percentage of methane (CH_4). The energy content is low, about 150 Btu per cu ft.

thermal efficiency: the ratio of the usable energy recovered to the total energy in the material burned or converted.

TOSCO: The Oil Shale Corporation.

TVA: the Tennessee Valley Authority, a government-financed corporation charged with the preservation and development of the valley of the Tennessee river.

References

1. Salaff, Stephen. *The Bulletin of the Atomic Scientists* (September 1980), pp. 18-23.
2. *Science* Vol. 209 (August 22, 1980), pp. 884-889.
3. Gofman, John, and Arthur R. Tamplin. *Poisoned Power* (Emmaus, PA: Rodale Press, 1971), pp. 41-44.
4. Reed, C. B. *Fuels, Minerals and Human Survival* (Ann Arbor, MI: Ann Arbor Science Publishers, Inc., 1975), pp. 115-143.
5. Cheremisinoff, Paul N., and Thomas C. Regino. *Principles and Applications of Solar Energy* (Ann Arbor, MI: Ann Arbor Science Publishers, Inc., 1979).
6. *Solar Energy as a National Energy Resource* (College Park, MD: The University of Maryland, 1972).
7. Yen, T. F. *Recycling and Disposal of Solid Wastes* (Ann Arbor, MI: Ann Arbor Science Publishers, Inc., 1974).
8. *U.S. News & World Report* (April 13, 1981), p. 40d.
9. *Time* (August 20, 1979), p. 42.
10. von Friesen, Sten. Personal communication (May 1980).
11. Dollezhal, N., and Y. Koryakin. *The Bulletin of the Atomic Scientists* (January 1980), pp. 33-37.
12. *Time* (January 22, 1979), p. 74.
13. Belnap, D. F. *Austin American-Statesman* (February 17, 1980), p. D4.
14. Krugman, Hartmut. *The Bulletin of the Atomic Scientists* (February 1981), pp. 33,34,36.

15. Los Angeles Times Service. *Austin American-Statesman* (February 26, 1981), p. A10.
16. Freeman, S. David. *Austin American-Statesman* (February 14, 1981), p. B9.
17. Pollock, Richard. *Austin American-Statesman* (March 18, 1981), p. A1.
18. Engler, Robert. *The Nation* (April 18, 1981), p. 458.
19. Averitt, Paul. In: *United States Mineral Resources*, U.S. Geological Survey Professional Paper 820 (Washington, DC: U.S. Government Printing Office, 1973).
20. U.S. Bureau of Mines. *Mineral Yearbook*, (Washington, DC: U.S. Government Printing Office, annual).
21. U.S. Department of Energy. Personal communication (March 1980).
22. *Scientific Encyclopedia* (New York: Van Nostrand Reinhold Company, 1976).
23. *Petroleum Facts and Figures* (New York: American Petroleum Institute, annual).
24. Perry, Robert H., and Cecil H. Chilton. *Chemical Engineers' Handbook* (New York: McGraw-Hill Book Company, 1973).
25. *Energy Outlook 1980-2000* (Houston, TX: Exxon Company, U.S.A., 1979).
26. *U.S. News & World Report* (April 6, 1981), p. 57.
27. Associated Press. *Austin American-Statesman* (February 14, 1980), p. G7.
28. *Survey of Current Business* (February 1980).
29. *Science* Vol. 208 (May 30, 1980), p. 1008.
30. Gulf Oil Corporation. *San Antonio Express* (April 4, 1980), p. 1-C.
31. *Encyclopedia of Science and Technology* (New York: McGraw-Hill Book Company, 1977).
32. *Time* (September 18, 1978), p. 102.
33. Barnaby, Frank. *The Bulletin of the Atomic Scientists* (April 1981), pp. 10,11.
34. Cooper, Hal. *Austin American-Statesman* (March 25, 1979), p. A10.

35. *Science* Vol. 182 (December 28, 1973), p. 1302.
36. *Construction Equipment* (March 1980), p. 47.
37. Hight, Bruce. *Austin American-Statesman* (April 17, 1980), p. B7.
38. Ryman, W. P. et al.
39. *Time* (May 19, 1980), p. 81.
40. *Coal Age* (May 1977), p. 79.
41. *Time* (June 2, 1980), p. 59.
42. *The Atlantic Monthly* (May 1980), p. 92.
43. Goldstein, Walter. *The Bulletin of the Atomic Scientists* (November 1979), p. 7.
44. *U.S. News & World Report* (April 7, 1980), p. 73.
45. *Time* (February 4, 1980), p. 71.
46. New York Times Service. *Austin American-Statesman* (May 22, 1980), p. A1.
47. Associated Press. *Austin American-Statesman* (June 27, 1980), p. A8.
48. *Energy and the Future* (Washington, DC: American Association for the Advancement of Science, 1973), p. 23.
49. Perry, Harry. *Scientific American* Vol. 230 (March 1974), pp. 19-25.
50. *Oil & Gas Journal* (November 26, 1979), p. 29.
51. *U.S. News & World Report* (September 29, 1980), pp. 42,43.
52. *Synfuels* (February 8, 1980), p. 2.
53. *Oil & Gas Journal* (October 29, 1979), p. 91.
54. *Oil & Gas Journal* (December 10, 1979), p. 42.
55. *The National Geographic Special Report* (February 1981), pp. 86,87.
56. Mueller, Lee. *Lexington Herald-Leader* (August 24, 1980), p. Coal-3.
57. Los Angeles Times Service. *Austin American-Statesman* (June 12, 1980), p. E2.
58. Yen, T. F. *Science and Technology of Oil Shale* (Ann Arbor, MI: Ann Arbor Science Publishers, Inc., 1976), pp. 47-64.

59. *Nova*, documentary aired by the Public Broadcasting Service (April 21, 1981).
60. *Time* (July 30, 1979).
61. Barnet, R. J. *The New Yorker* (March 17, 1980), p. 64.
62. Osborn, E. F. *Science* Vol. 183 (February 8, 1974), pp. 479,480.
63. *Time* (January 28, 1974), p. 35.
64. Edgar, T. F., and J. T. Richardson. *Resources and Utilization of Texas Lignite* (Austin, TX: The State of Texas, 1974).
65. *Handbook of Chemistry and Physics*, 53rd ed. (Cleveland, OH: CRC Press, Inc., 1973).
66. Hammer, Armand, Chicago Tribune Service. *Austin American-Statesman* (February 25, 1981), p. D12.
67. *Science* Vol. 182 (November 2, 1973), pp. 456-458.
68. Cheremisinoff, Nicholas P. *Gasohol for Energy Production* (Ann Arbor, MI: Ann Arbor Science Publishers, Inc., 1979), pp. 56,69.
69. *Synfuels* (February 8, 1980), p. 7.
70. *Science* Vol. 189 (July 11, 1975), pp. 128-129.
71. *Science* Vol. 211 (February 27, 1981), pp. 903-906.
72. Muffler, L. J. P. In: *United States Mineral Resources*, U.S. Geological Survey Professional Paper 820 (Washington, DC: U.S. Government Printing Office, 1973), pp. 251-261.
73. Kirby, Ralph C., and Andrew S. Prokopovitsch. *Science* Vol. 191 (February 20, 1976), p. 714.
74. Loraine, John A. *The Bulletin of the Atomic Scientists* Vol. 37 (March 1981), p. 19.
75. Reed, C. B. *Growth and Immigration* (in preparation), Chapter 11.
76. Noll, Roger G. *Science* Vol. 208 (May 16, 1980), p. 702.
77. Kappuls, William, Texas Gulf Chemical Company. Personal communication (April 16, 1981).

Index